Wind

Joy Palmer

Franklin Watts
London • New York • Sydney • Toronto

© 1992 Franklin Watts

Franklin Watts
96 Leonard Street
London EC2A 4RH

Franklin Watts Australia
14 Mars Road
Lane Cove
NSW 2060

UK ISBN: 0 7496 0644 4

10 9 8 7 6 5 4 3 2 1

Series editor: A. Patricia Sechi
Design: Shaun Barlow
Cover design: Edward Kinsey
Artwork: Michael Lye
Cover artwork: Hugh Dixon
Picture research: Ambreen Husain

A CIP catalogue record for this book
is available from the British Library

Printed in Italy by G. Canale & C. SpA

Contents

What is wind?

Wind is air which moves. We do not usually think of air as having any weight but it has. Because air has weight it also has **pressure**. Air in upper layers of the **atmosphere** presses down on air below. In some places the pressure can be higher or lower than in others. Wind occurs when air flows from an area of high pressure to an area of low pressure.

▽ Wind is moving air. It rustles leaves and bends branches.

A windy day

Weather forecasters tell us about high and low air pressure. They talk about **highs** and **depressions**. Depressions are areas of low pressure. They often bring rain and storms. Air may move into areas of low pressure bringing winds. Strong winds can make things around us move. Tree branches bend in the wind and leaves blow across the ground.

▽ Weather forecasts can tell us how strong winds will be.

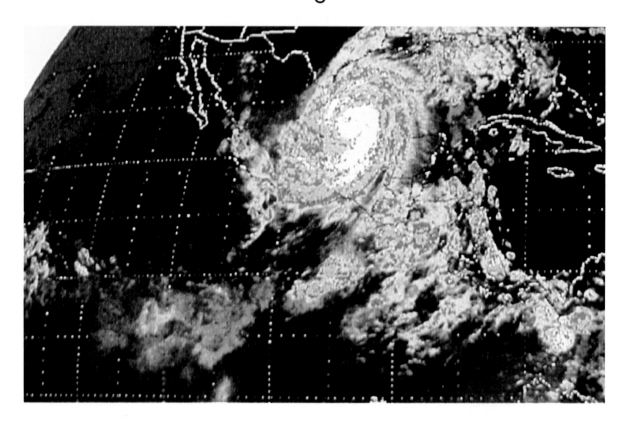

4

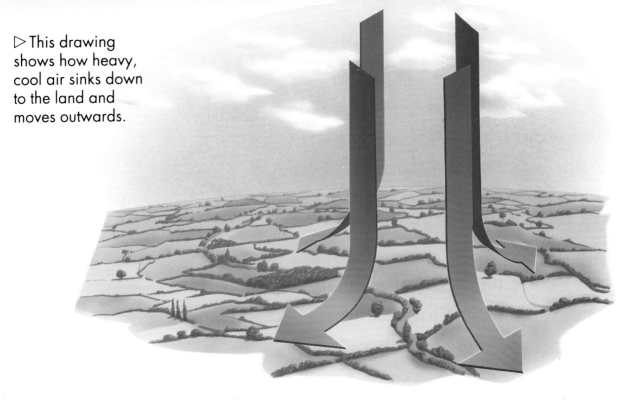

▷ This drawing shows how heavy, cool air sinks down to the land and moves outwards.

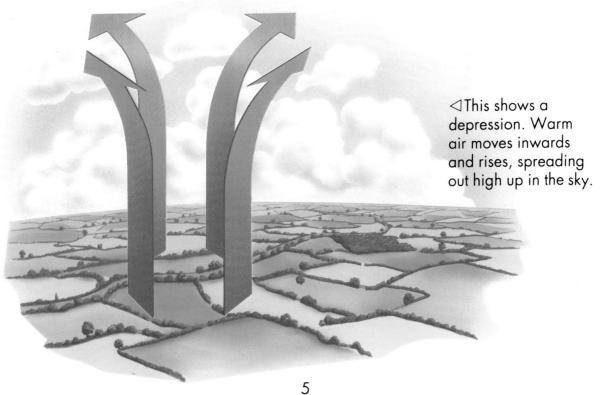

◁ This shows a depression. Warm air moves inwards and rises, spreading out high up in the sky.

Measuring the wind

▷ An anemometer is an instrument which measures wind speed.

A scale is used to **estimate** the speed of the wind by looking at the world around us. It is called the Beaufort Scale. It measures wind as a force from 0 to 12. At force 0 there is no wind. Smoke from a chimney rises straight up into the air. Force 12 means that a **hurricane** is blowing. This is the strongest wind of all and causes great damage.

▽ The Beaufort Scale measures the force of the wind by looking at its effects around us.

Force 2
A gentle breeze. Leaves rustle and you feel the wind on your face.

Force 6
A strong breeze is blowing. Umbrellas may turn inside out.

Force 8-9
Gales. Twigs break off. In strong gales chimneys may be damaged.

Force 12
A hurricane is blowing. Trees are uprooted and great damage is caused.

Hurricanes

Some winds are dangerous and can cause terrible damage. Hurricanes are very strong winds. They begin as small thunderstorms over **tropical** oceans. As heat and warm water are taken in, the hurricane grows larger. Differences in air pressure cause huge spiralling winds.

▷ This photograph was taken from a satellite. It shows the whirling pattern of the wind.

▽ A hurricane swirls round in a spiral. In the centre of the spiral there is no wind at all. This is called the 'eye' of the storm.

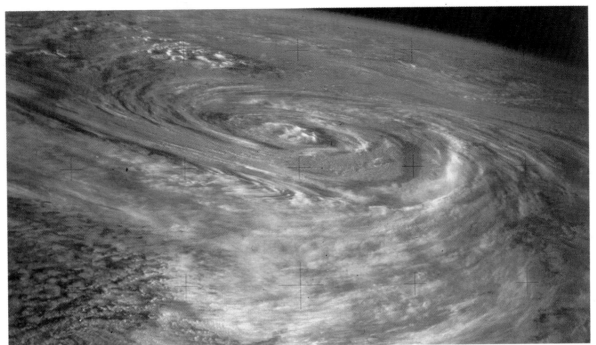

▷ Smashed houses
and uprooted trees
show the path of the
hurricane.

Whirlwinds

Tornadoes are violent, whirling wind storms. They usually occur during very heavy rain, thunder and lightning. They begin over land where cold, dry air meets warm, wet air. If the wind starts swirling in tight circles, a tornado is formed. The whirling air of a tornado spins at great speed. It can toss cars and buildings high into the air and then smash them to the ground.

▽ A whirling tornado can lift trees or heavy vehicles into its funnel.

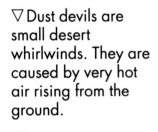

▽ Dust devils are small desert whirlwinds. They are caused by very hot air rising from the ground.

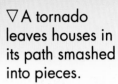

▽ A tornado leaves houses in its path smashed into pieces.

Winds at sea

Sea breezes occur near the coast. On warm, sunny days the land heats up more quickly than the sea. Warm air rises over the land, and cool breezes move in to take its place. At night the land cools more quickly than the sea, and breezes blow out to the ocean. Oceans never stop moving, partly because the air above them is always on the move.

▷ When there is only a little wind, small waves and ripples are formed on the water.

▽ The wind can make huge waves which smash against the shoreline.

▷ During the day, cool breezes blow from the sea over the land. At night they blow from the land to the sea.

Dust and sandstorms

When wind blows over dry or dusty land, soil is swept high into the air. Dust storms may take all the good soil away, leaving nowhere for plants to grow. This is called **soil erosion**. In the desert, strong winds cause sandstorms which cover plants and buildings with sand. The wind blows sand into banks, too, which move with the changing winds.

▽ The sky darkens as the air fills with grit and sand during a sandstorm.

▷ Sand and soil carried by the wind wear away rock surfaces.

◁ The wind blows sand banks in different directions and buries buildings.

15

Plants and the wind

Strong winds batter trees into odd shapes, especially near the sea. Plants do not blow away in the wind. Their long roots keep them firmly in the ground. Some plants use the wind to spread their **pollen**. This is the yellow dust inside flowers. The wind can carry pollen from one plant to another. Other plants use the wind to scatter their seeds.

▷ The springy trunks of these palm trees help them to bend in the wind.

▽ Trees in windy places are often bent and twisted.

16

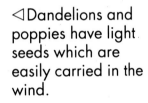

◁Dandelions and poppies have light seeds which are easily carried in the wind.

△Sycamore seeds have wings which spin and travel through the air.

17

Animals in the wind

Many animals are covered in fur or hair which trap heat. Like us, animals enjoy a cool wind on a hot day. Some animals, such as birds, can make use of the wind when they fly. When warm air rises, it helps birds soar and glide. Animals, including camels, also protect themselves from the wind.

▷ Camels have two sets of eyelashes, and nostrils which close to protect them in sandstorms.

▽ Part of the Portuguese man-of-war's body floats above the water and acts like a sail.

△ A tornado has been known to pluck the feathers from a chicken!

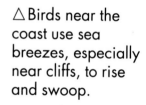

△ Birds near the coast use sea breezes, especially near cliffs, to rise and swoop.

Winds around the world

Air moves round the earth all the time. The earth is much warmer near the **equator** than it is at the poles. This creates winds as cool air rushes in to replace rising warm air. The earth spins around so winds do not blow in a straight line from cold to warm. The main winds around the world are named after the direction from which they blow.

▽ Some winds, such as monsoons, blow in just one part of the world. They bring heavy rains, especially to Asia.

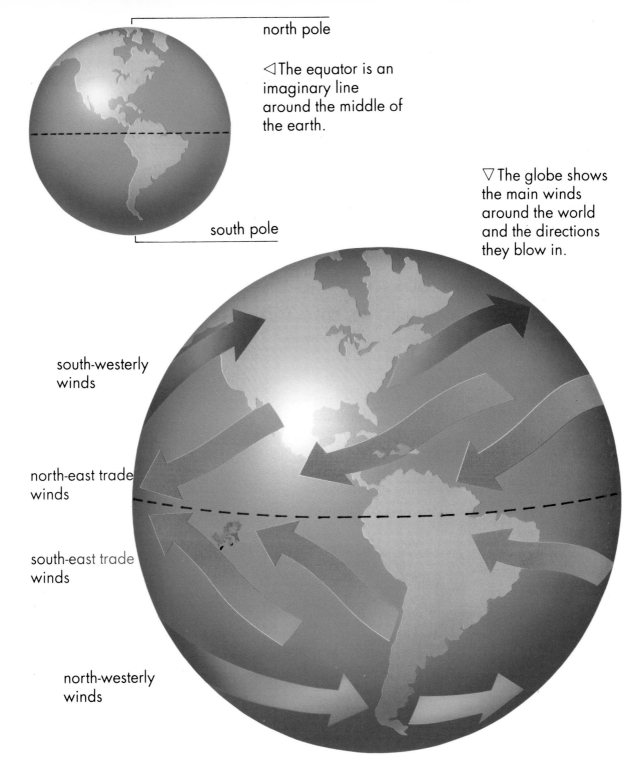

north pole

◁ The equator is an imaginary line around the middle of the earth.

south pole

▽ The globe shows the main winds around the world and the directions they blow in.

south-westerly winds

north-east trade winds

south-east trade winds

north-westerly winds

21

Living with the wind

Strong winds can be dangerous. They blow roof tiles and branches to the ground. But people have found ways of living with the wind. **Engineers** design bridges and buildings so that they will not fall down in powerful winds. **Double-glazing** stops the wind blowing through gaps in windows and making our homes cold.

▷ In northern Europe people on the beach sit in wickerwork chairs to protect themselves from strong sea breezes.

▽ The shape and materials used for buildings and bridges makes them able to stand up to strong winds.

Wind energy

Moving wind has **energy**. People have used its power for hundreds of years. Windmills were used for grinding grain or pumping water. But today, modern windmills are used to turn wind power into electricity. There will always be winds. They are a clean and useful source of power.

▷ Hundreds of windmills on this wind farm provide electricity to nearby towns.

◁ Windmills were used in the past to grind grain for making flour.

▷ This kind of windmill is used to pump water.

Using the wind

Wind is one of the most powerful forces on the earth. It can damage and destroy, but it can also be used for good purposes. Some sailing boats still rely on the power of the wind. We can also use the wind for everyday tasks.

▽ The sails on this modern tanker are made of metal. They help to save fuel.

▷ Many people use the wind to dry wet washing. It saves using electric dryers.

▽ Sailing boats are still used in some countries to carry goods.

27

Enjoying the wind

Light winds can give us a lot of fun. Have you ever flown a kite on a windy day? Winds send yachts scudding across the water. Sea breezes help windsurfers skim over the waves. Up in the sky some light aircraft, such as **hang gliders**, rely on the power of the wind to stay up in the air.

▽ On a windy day, the wind carries a kite high into the sky.

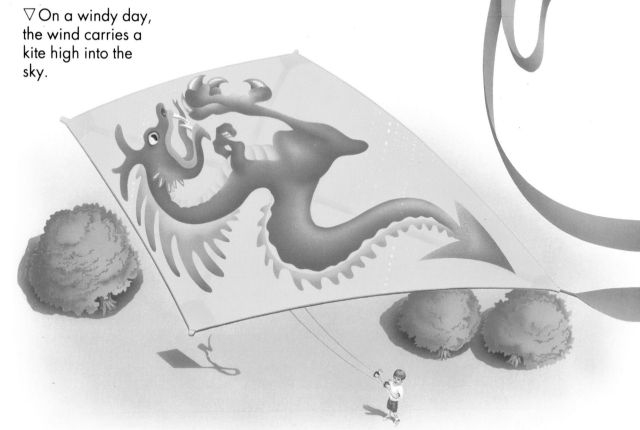

◁Like some birds a hang glider makes use of air currents.

▷ The sport of windsurfing relies on the power of the wind to drive a sail over the waves.

Things to do

- Make a weather vane. Ask an adult to push a knitting needle into a cork. Put the cork into a bottle. Place a pen top on the end of the needle. Make a paper arrow. Tape it to the pen top. Write the compass points on pieces of paper and stick them to the bottle. With a compass check that they are in the right place. Now find out which way the wind blows.

- Make a windmill. Cut a piece of paper about 16cm square. Fold the paper to make a triangle. Fold the triangle in half. Open out the paper and cut half way along each fold. Fold one corner into the centre. Leave the next corner and fold the one after into the centre. Repeat this round the paper. Put a pin through the centre and fix the windmill to a stick.

Glossary

air pressure The weight of the air.

atmosphere The air around the earth.

depression A low, or an area of low pressure.

double-glazing A window which has two panes of glass to make a double window.

energy The power to do work and to drive machines.

engineer A person who plans the making of bridges, roads and machines and checks that they are built properly.

equator An imaginary line which runs around the middle of the earth.

estimate To guess or work out the amount or size of something.

fuel Substances which are burned to produce heat or power. Coal and oil are fuels.

hang glider A large kite in which a person glides down to earth.

high An area of high pressure.

hurricane A very strong wind. It can cause great damage.

pollen The yellow dust on a flower. It is carried to other flowers by insects and the wind and helps to make seeds.

sea breeze A light wind which blows inland from the cool sea to warm land.

soil erosion When soil is blown away by wind or washed away by the rain.

tropical A word used to describe places near the equator.

Index